The Book of Dreams Come True

A JOURNAL OF SELF-DISCOVERY, GOALS, AND MANIFESTATION

BRYN DONOVAN

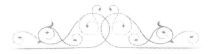

Say Hello to the Rest of Your Life.

Today is the perfect day to reconnect with your true self and to dream big about where you are headed. If you've been going through a stressful or difficult time…if you're beginning a new phase in your life, such as a new year, a birthday, a graduation, a move, or a change in your career or your relationships…or if you just feel that you could use some fresh inspiration…this journal is for you, right now.

You deserve to take some time with your thoughts, feelings, and dreams. This journal is designed to help you illuminate your possibilities for joy in the moment and success in the future. No matter what you've been through, you can make the rest of your life the best of your life.

Reality begins with your imagination. Words and ideas can change your mindset…and when you change your mindset, you change your life. Ignite your creativity, write yourself free from whatever's holding you back, and find the motivation to live on a whole new level.

This journal includes writing prompts designed to help you get rid of some of the negativity that's crept into your thinking, whether from your past, from other people, or from messages you receive from society. Even more writing prompts will help you replace that negativity with gratitude, fun, hope, and joy.

The list-making in the journal will lead you to think beyond the obvious. You'll also encounter exercises in which you're asked to pick a number between one and twenty-five and then write about the word assigned to that number. What are these all about? The random choices stretch your creativity. But who knows? They may not be so random, after all. You may find they uncover real truths about you and your destiny.

I've also included blank pages here and there so you can capture other thoughts, lists, memories, wishes, or intentions. Sometimes one writing exercise will lead to other ideas!

More than anything else, this journal is about your dreams. It will help you understand what it is you truly want in life…small things and big things, too. You want to be really clear about this, because when you're bold enough to believe in your dreams, they often do come true.

Some people believe that positive thinking attracts positive things, people, and events. I can tell you that in my personal experience, it certainly *seems* that way. When I've dedicated time to thinking positive thoughts and reflecting on my dreams, I've seen amazing things happen. Just as important, I've taken enjoyment in everyday living. When I've fallen away from this practice, life has become more of a struggle. I began creating the exercises in this journal to get my happiness back again, and as it started to work, I realized I wanted to share them with other people, too.

One thing is for sure: when you set your mind on goals and believe they're possible, your subconscious mind goes to work, figuring out ways to make them happen.

Skeptical? That's understandable! Difficulties in your past or present may have left you feeling bruised. Some of these pages even address that! But give yourself a chance. Even if some pages feel strange or uncomfortable at first, you may respond to them in ways that surprise you.

You don't have to do all these pages, of course. You can do them in order, flip around and do them at random, or start with the ones that appeal to you most. You might want to do one every morning or every evening, or you might want to take a weekend to do a bunch at once.

You're an extraordinary person, and you were not made for an ordinary life. Get to know yourself, believe in yourself, and light up your days or years ahead…your best ones yet.

This book belongs to

——————————— Maggi ———————————,

whose dreams are going to come true.

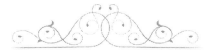

Introducing Myself

What's your name? Write it vertically down the page next to the example below. Then, for each letter that spells out your name, write a positive descriptor that describes you beginning with that letter. Like this:

Young at Heart

Optimistic

Unique

Radiant

Nonconforming

Adventurous

Magnetic

Energized

Magnificent

Adventurous

Genuine

Grateful

Imaginative

If you need a little help, use the words on the next page for inspiration. It's not a complete list!

A – awesome, ambitious, active, adventurous, adaptable, affectionate

B – brilliant, brave, bold, balanced, beautiful, bookish

C – creative, compassionate, confident, courageous, considerate, charming

D – determined, dynamic, dependable, devoted, daring, decisive, delightful

E – enthusiastic, energetic, encouraging, excellent, easy-going, efficient

F – fantastic, fun, friendly, faithful, fit, frugal, funny, free-spirited, fabulous

G – generous, grateful, gregarious, gentle, genuine, graceful, gorgeous, great

H – hilarious, helpful, hard-working, hot, honorable, honest

I – intelligent, individualistic, independent, intuitive, imaginative, impressive

J – joyful, jovial, jaw-dropping, just

K – kind, knowledgeable, kooky (kooky is good!)

L – loving, loveable, loyal, level-headed, lively, legendary

M – magnificent, magnetic, meticulous, magical

N – nice, natural, nature-loving, neat, nonconforming, nonjudgmental

O – outstanding, optimistic, original, organized, open-minded, observant

P – patient, powerful, passionate, persistent, polite, practical, persuasive

Q – quick-witted, queenly, quirky, quality-minded

R – remarkable, rational, romantic, radiant, resourceful, ravishing, regal

S – smart, strong, savvy, sensible, successful, sensational, spectacular

T – terrific, talented, trustworthy, tenacious, thoughtful, thrilling

U – unique, understanding, unflappable, unselfish, unbreakable

V – valuable, valiant, virtuous, vivacious, vigorous, vibrant

W – wonderful, wise, warm, witty, wild, wholesome, warriorlike

X – X-cellent, X-citing, X-uberant, X-troverted, X-ceptional

Y – young, young at heart, yummy, yes-minded

Z – zany, Zen, zippy, zingy, zeroed in on success

Put your two favorite positive adjectives from your name
in the blanks below and write about them.

Here's one way that I'm ___Adventurous___:

I always want to try new things out.
Like going to new places, trying new hobbies,
and kind of trying out new foods. In
my prospective I call that adventurous. ★

Here's one way that I'm ___Grateful___:

Whenever I get something I always
thank the person who gave it to me
and I use that gift as much as
possable. But I don't always feel
grateful.

"Boom"

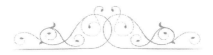

My Brilliant Future

This is to help you think about all the possibilities that lie ahead of you! Quick, choose three numbers between one and twenty-five.

Now flip the page and see which three words you chose. They may be in your near future!

Below, write about what those three words might mean to you or how they might manifest.

_____ Wealth _____

(word 1)

This might mean I will have a good job and not worry about money to much.

_____ Relief _____

(word 2)

This might mean that something that has been troubling me will go away.

_____ Nature _____

(word 3)

I just need to go out and take a nature walk and appreciate it.

1. restoration

2. friends

3. ocean

4. romance

5. breakthrough

6. admiration

7. wealth

8. adventure

9. new job

10. transformation

11. beauty

12. victory

13. health

14. happy family

15. relief

16. windfall

17. travel

18. fame

19. nature

20. freedom

21. success

22. fitness

23. happiness

24. sunshine

25. renewal

Is there one on the list that you didn't pick…but that you want to have in your future? Change your fortune by envisioning it. Write about that one below, in *present tense*…as if you already have it.

Here's how I have _____ relief _____ in my life:

Now that I knew that my whole family is healthy and happy and can not fake themself through life. I feel so much better. They don't have to fake a smile or a laught anymore. They are stopping all the bad thing in their life. They will be a happier, healthier, nicer, and better person. :)

Not Really

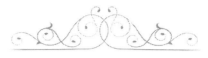

My Bio

When you set up a social media account, you often have to write a very short bio or description of yourself. But whether you're on social media or not, writing a bio is a way to connect with who you are and how you present yourself to the world.

Scroll through your phone and choose three emoji that pertain to you or represent you personally. List them here and write about what they represent. (See the two examples given.)

butterfly emoji ---- ▶ *becoming my better self*

clapper board emoji ---- ▶ *aspiring movie director*

1. Snail Emoji ---- ▶ Finding what I like

2. ---- ▶

3. ---- ▶

Now write some short adjective + noun phrases that describe you right now. (See the examples given.)

snarky blonde　　　　　　　　　　　*amused gen Xer*
over-caffeinated mom　　　　　　　　*loveable weirdo*

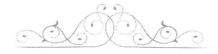

The Story of My Life

If your life story was made into a novel, what would be some of the titles the publisher would consider? Try out a few.

examples:

Coffee and Glitter

The Pittsburgh Dreamer

_____

_____

_____

If your life story was made into a movie, what would be the genre...*if* you were already living your ideal life? Action, comedy, romance?

_____

Who would play you in the movie? List a couple of people the casting director would consider.

_____

_____

What songs would be on the soundtrack for the movie?

_____

_____

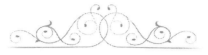

Setting Boundaries

Some of us are good at setting healthy limits in our relationships to other people and our work. But some of us struggle with this. When we don't have good limits, it can wear us out and be hard on our self-esteem.

I'm going to be respectful toward these people, but I'm not going to take personal responsibility for their happiness, because that's not my job:

_____

_____

_____

I'm not going to handle this job or this situation all by myself, because other people should share that responsibility with me:

_____

_____

_____

I'm going to respect this person's need for privacy: _____

By doing this: _____

_____

I'm going to respect my own privacy by doing this: _____

_____

_____

_____

_____

I'm going to make sure, to the best of my ability, that I'm the only one who makes choices about my own body, clothing, etc., by doing this:

_____

_____

_____

When I need to rant, here's where I'm *not* going to do it, because that doesn't serve me well:

_____

_____

_____

Instead, when I need to rant, I'm going to do this:

_____

_____

_____

_____

_____

_____

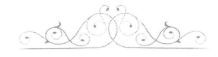

Success Beyond Belief

Many of us have learned false and toxic beliefs about **money, work, and success**. These beliefs limit our ability to live an abundant and joyful life.

On this page and the next one, you'll write out a toxic belief about money, work, or success. Then you'll cross it out and write a positive new belief you can embrace. After that, you'll write down one possible action you could take (no obligation here—it's just a thought), assuming that positive new belief is true. Here are three examples of how this works. Even if one of these examples fits you, the possible action will depend on you and your life.

Toxic Belief: I'll never be out of debt.
New Belief: I'm getting out of debt sooner rather than later.
Possible Action: Make a wall chart to track monthly reduction of debt.

Toxic Belief: I'm too much of an oddball to be successful.
New Belief: I'm truly original, and that's one reason I'm becoming successful.
Possible Action: Take an online course in my preferred field.

Toxic Belief: I will never succeed because I've screwed up too much already.
New Belief: I have learned a lot, which will help me succeed in the future.
Possible Action: Take someone whose success you admire to lunch and ask them for advice.

You get the idea. Now give it a try!

Toxic Belief: _____

New Belief: _____

Possible Action: _____

Toxic Belief: _____

New Belief: _____

Possible Action: _____

Toxic Belief: _____

New Belief: _____

Possible Action: _____

Choose one of your new beliefs and write a little bit about how it's going to help you in the long term.

_____

_____

_____

_____

_____

_____

_____

_____

_____

_____

_____

_____

_____

_____

_____

_____

_____

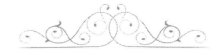

Happiness Beyond Belief

Many of us also have toxic beliefs about **relationships, health,** and **happiness.**

Some of us grew up hearing negative things about ourselves. Some of us know people right now who say things about us that are completely untrue and unfair. Social media, magazines, books, movies, and TV may also give you dispiriting or limiting messages.

Do the same thing again here: write out the toxic belief about relationships, health, and happiness and then cross it out. Write the positive new belief and one possible action you could take assuming that new belief is true. Here are three examples!

Toxic Belief: I'm not attractive enough to find a spouse.

New Belief: I'm beautiful inside and out, and I'll probably meet my soulmate soon.

Possible Action: Walk into every room like you're an arriving celebrity, and smile.

Toxic Belief: I'll never be healthy.

New Belief: I'm getting healthier.

Possible Action: Go to bed at a decent hour every night.

Toxic Belief: I don't know how to talk to people.

New Belief: I'm getting better at talking to people all the time.

Possible Action: Volunteer once a week and talk to other volunteers.

Toxic Belief: _____

New Belief: _____

Possible Action: _____

Toxic Belief: _____

New Belief: _____

Possible Action: _____

Toxic Belief: _____

New Belief: _____

Possible Action: _____

Choose one of your new beliefs, and write a little bit about how it's going to help you in the long term.

_____

_____

_____

_____

_____

_____

_____

_____

_____

_____

_____

_____

_____

_____

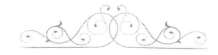

My Areas of Expertise

What are some things that you know a lot about...that might surprise some people?

_____

_____

_____

_____

_____

If you were brought in to teach something to a bunch of ten-year-olds, what would you teach them?

_____

_____

_____

_____

_____

Write about a time that you taught something to someone else.

_____

_____

_____

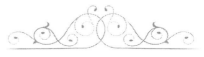

Enough is Enough

This page is about getting rid of something.

It may have been with you for a very long time, or it might've shown up in the past few years. That guilt or shame you have about something. That worry you keep chewing on. That resentment or regret you lug around, everywhere you go...so heavy, you're exhausted before the day is over. It's taken enough out of you already. Enough of your energy, your hope, and your joy.

Don't name it on this page, because you're getting rid of it, so you don't need a lasting reminder. Name it in your head, and call it "It" on paper.

Now describe, as creatively as you can, how you're going to get rid of It. Set it on fire? Throw it in the ocean? Launch it into space? Write about how you feel as you watch it disappear from your life, and how you will feel when you're free of it.

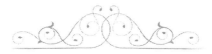

But Wait...There's More

While you're at it, let some smaller things go, too. (It's okay to name these.) If they're keeping you from being happy or being the best version of yourself, it's time to leave them behind.

I'm tired of pretending this:

_____

_____

_____

I'm tired of wasting way too much time on this:

_____

_____

_____

Here's something I'm not going to beat myself up about anymore:

_____

_____

_____

I am done holding myself to this completely unrealistic expectation:

_____

_____

_____

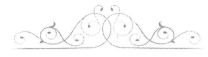

I Reject This Advice

What is one of the worst pieces of advice you've ever read…or that anyone has ever delivered to you personally? Write down what it was, and write about why it's not the right advice for you…or, maybe, not the right advice for anyone. (You can do more than one!)

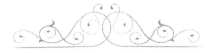

I Remember This Advice

What is one of the *best* pieces of advice you've ever gotten...or one of the best pieces of advice you've ever read? Maybe it's time to revisit it again! Write about it below. (If nothing comes to mind, feel free to write out some advice to yourself.)

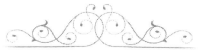

I Am a Survivor

Write about one or two difficult things that you've already survived in your lifetime.

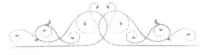

Unbreakable

I can handle rejections without being crushed, because

_____

_____

I don't let my past traumas define me, because

_____

_____

Write about a time you persisted.

_____

_____

_____

_____

_____

_____

_____

_____

_____

_____

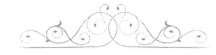

Encouragement From My Favorite Famous People

Imagine that you're sitting down with three famous people, dead or alive. (They can absolutely be fictional characters!) They're people you would choose for mentors if you could. They came to visit you because they think you're an incredible person and they want to support you, make you feel better, and help you succeed. Each one has words of encouragement for you. Write down their names and what each one says to you below.

_____

(person one)

_____

_____

_____

_____

(person two)

_____

_____

_____

_____

(person three)

_____

_____

_____

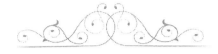

What a Wonderful World

Write about one (or more) of the most beautiful buildings you've ever visited—in real life, or in a book, TV show, or movie.

_____

_____

_____

_____

_____

_____

_____

Write about one (or more) of the most beautiful natural places you've ever experienced—in real life, or in a book, TV show, or movie.

_____

_____

_____

_____

_____

_____

_____

Now, just take two minutes to close your eyes and imagine yourself in one of these places. Imagine the sights, the sounds, the smells, and the sensations.

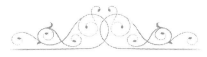

Beauty All Around

Make a list of 50 more things you think are beautiful or enjoyable to see, hear, touch, taste, or smell.

1. _____
2. _____
3. _____
4. _____
5. _____
6. _____
7. _____
8. _____
9. _____
10. _____
11. _____
12. _____
13. _____
14. _____
15. _____
16. _____
17. _____
18. _____

19. _____
20. _____
21. _____
22. _____
23. _____
24. _____
25. _____
26. _____
27. _____
28. _____
29. _____
30. _____
31. _____
32. _____
33. _____
34. _____
35. _____
36. _____
37. _____
38. _____
39. _____
40. _____
41. _____
42. _____
43. _____
44. _____
45. _____

46. _____

47. _____

48. _____

49. _____

50. _____

Write about a memory you have about one (or more) of these things.

_____

_____

_____

_____

_____

_____

_____

_____

_____

_____

_____

_____

_____

_____

_____

_____

_____

_____

_____

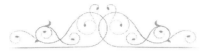

Getting All the
Good Things Back

These pages will help you remember who you were as a child, what you loved and valued, and what spoke to you. The world may have encouraged you to set aside some essential parts of yourself at some point over the years. By reconnecting with the things you once loved, you can restore your true self.

Here are three books, TV shows, or movies I loved in my childhood or adolescence:

1. ....

2. ....

3. ....

Here's what I loved about them:

_____

_____

_____

_____

_____

_____

_____

_____

Here are three things I loved to do as a kid or a teenager:

1. _____

2. _____

3. _____

Here's why I loved doing them:

_____

_____

_____

_____

_____

_____

_____

_____

_____

_____

_____

_____

_____

_____

_____

_____

_____

_____

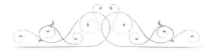

"Never Too Late to Have a Happy Childhood" Checklist

Check all of the "childish" things that you might decide you want to do as an adult.

- ☑ Dance around the living room.
- ☑ Watch cartoons on Sunday morning.
- ☑ Watch animated Disney movies.
- ☑ Color in a coloring book.
- ☑ Play with Play-Doh.
- ☑ Eat sugary cereal…the kind that comes with a prize at the bottom of the box.
- ☑ Build something out of Legos.
- ☑ Blow soap bubbles.
- ☑ Jump in a pile of leaves.
- ☐ Play by a creek.
- ☑ Jump in a puddle.
- ☑ Have a water balloon fight.
- ☑ Run through a sprinkler.
- ☐ Keep toys in the bathtub.
- ☑ Go to bed with a stuffed animal.
- ☑ Climb a tree.
- ☐ Go barefoot.

Add additional ideas if you like:

_____

_____

_____

_____

_____

_____

_____

_____

_____

Write about one or two (or more) happy memories from your childhood or adolescence.

_____

_____

_____

_____

_____

_____

_____

_____

_____

Now write about happy memories from the past year or two. Even if it's been rough, there are probably a few good times that stand out.

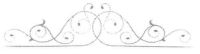

I Am Thankful

Write a prayer of gratitude or a meditation about all the things you are grateful for today.

_____

_____

_____

_____

_____

_____

_____

_____

_____

_____

_____

_____

_____

_____

_____

_____

_____

Write a prayer of gratitude or a meditation about all the good things you know are coming your way.

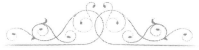

Truer Words
Were Never Spoken

Write down some of the compliments you've received in your lifetime, big or small. They can be from when you were four years old...or they can be from today! If you want, you can also make note of who gave you each compliment.

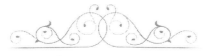

My Compliments

Since compliments can have such a positive impact on people, write down the names of a few people in your life you'd like to compliment and the compliments you want to give them.

_____

(name of person)

_____

_____

_____

_____

_____

(name of person)

_____

_____

_____

_____

_____

(name of person)

_____

_____

_____

_____

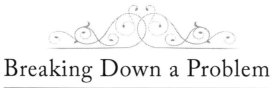

Breaking Down a Problem

Write down one difficulty or challenge in your life.

_____

_____

Is it something you're able and willing to walk away from or cut out of your life?

_____

_____

What are five reasons why it's a problem?

1. _____
2. _____
3. _____
4. _____
5. _____

What could you do to address one or more of those reasons in order to make your life better, even if the problem doesn't go away?

_____

_____

_____

_____

_____

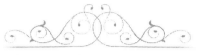

Animal Instincts

Animals symbolize different qualities for us. Bulls are stubborn. Swans are graceful. This is why so many sports teams choose animals for mascots…and so many people feel a personal affinity for certain animals.

Choose a number between one and twenty-five. Then flip the page to discover one of your animal symbols. You can think of this as a personal mascot, your patronus if you're a Harry Potter fan, or an animal that would go on your coat of arms, if you lived in medieval Europe. Give the animal a chance in your imagination: maybe it represents something you didn't know you needed.

But if you really want to, you can claim a different animal! It doesn't even have to be on the list.

Now write about it!

My animal is the ———————————————————.

For me, it represents:

_____

_____

_____

_____

_____

_____

_____

_____

_____

_____

1. eagle
2. dragon
3. rabbit
4. bear
5. honeybee
6. bat
7. tiger
8. fox
9. horse
10. dog
11. otter
12. peacock
13. wolf
14. cat
15. hummingbird
16. butterfly
17. unicorn
18. tortoise
19. firefly
20. lion
21. polar bear
22. bluebird
23. black panther
24. dolphin
25. deer

Write about a time you saw an animal in the wild.

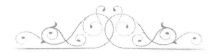

My Favorite Things

You deserve to enjoy life. Sometimes, we can get so busy with tasks or overwhelmed with worries that we forget to do that! This list is to remind you of some of the things that make you happy, so you stop and savor them...or go out of your way to enjoy them. This is another way of reminding yourself who you really are.

It is perfectly okay to write down more than one favorite for any of these. And if one of these doesn't pertain to you, cross it out and substitute another favorite thing!

Favorite day of the week: _Friday_

Favorite holiday: _Christmas_

Favorite season of the year: _Fall_

Favorite beverage order at a coffee shop: _Chai Tea_

Favorite alcoholic beverage: _____

Favorite vegetable: _Cucumber_

Favorite fruit: _Apples_

Favorite snack: _Star Puffs_

Favorite candy: _Sour Patch Kids_

Favorite dessert: _____

Favorite restaurant: _____

Favorite thing to have for dinner: _____

Favorite outfit I own right now: _Cardigin, T-shirt, black jeans_

Favorite thing to wear to bed: _T-shirt, socks_ ☺

Favorite fashion style (casual, boho, etc.): _Cottage Core, Dark Academic_

Favorite color to wear: _Black_

Favorite kind of shoe: _Converses_

Favorite game: _Animal Crossing_

Favorite way to get exercise: _Running_

Favorite sport to watch: _Baseball_

Favorite sports team: _No_

Favorite TV show right now: _My Hero Acadamia_

Favorite TV show of all time: _Hilda_

Favorite celebrity: _No_

Favorite genre of movie (action, comedy, etc.): _Adventure_

Favorite genre of book (biography, fantasy, etc.): _Fantasy, Adventure_

Favorite poem or prayer: _Snow ball_

Favorite motto or expression: _I dont know_

Favorite emoji: _Snail Emoji_

Favorite song: _Mary on a cross - Ghost_

Favorite sound (non-musical): _____

Favorite scent: _Cookie Batter_

Favorite tree: _____

Favorite flower: _____

Favorite landscape (mountains, beach, etc.): _Mountains_

Favorite fictional place: _____

Favorite store to shop at: _____

Favorite brand: _____

Favorite way to treat myself: _____

Favorite guilty pleasure: _____

More Favorite Things:

_____

_____

_____

_____

_____

_____

_____

_____

_____

_____

_____

_____

_____

_____

_____

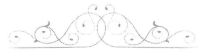

As I Wish

You can use your list of favorite things to give yourself preferential treatment. Think about small ways you can integrate your preferences into your everyday life. You could buy a notebook or a mug in your favorite color, treat yourself to your favorite coffee shop order every Thursday, and so on. Write about ways you might use your list here.

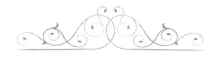

The World Needs Me

The world needs my _kindness_ .

Why? Because _the world is too mean_ .

People out there could use my _happiness_ .

Why? Because _people are very sad and need it_ .

_____Dad_____ depends on me for _cleaning_ .
(this person)

_____Mimi_____ appreciates my _kindness_ .
(this person)

_____Ryan_____ would be lost without my _kindness_ .
(this person)

Write about a time when someone appreciated your words or deeds.

_____

_____

_____

_____

_____

_____

_____

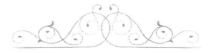

For the First Time in a Long Time

We all know that we take many things for granted. For instance, we may be so accustomed to certain things that it's hard to imagine life without them... things like having a family member or friend who cares about us, having enough food to eat, having clean water, having a physically healthy internal organ or body part, or being able to do a certain thing. This exercise is to remind you what a miracle these kinds of things really are.

In the blanks on this page and the next, write down three very basic things you are grateful for...things that are so fundamental, you hardly ever think about them.

For each one of them, imagine that you just received these gifts after going without them for a very long time. For instance, if you chose "having hot water," write about how good the hot water feels when you take a shower and lather up with soap.

_____

(thing I'm grateful for)

_____

(thing I'm grateful for)

_____
_____
_____
_____
_____

_____

(thing I'm grateful for)

_____
_____
_____
_____
_____

_____

(thing I'm grateful for)

_____
_____
_____
_____
_____

Always Victorious

Write about a triumph—large or small—that you achieved when you were younger.

_____

_____

_____

_____

Write about an accomplishment—large or small—that you achieved in the past year.

_____

_____

_____

_____

Write about an accomplishment—large or very, _very_ small—that you achieved in the past _week_.

_____

_____

_____

_____

Now write about a huge triumph…as if you had already achieved it. Write about what it is and how you feel about it. You can also write about what others say to you about it, how you celebrate, or what you do as a result of your accomplishment.

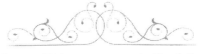

My Elemental Self

In past times, many people believed there were four elements.

- Air represented communication, intellect, and inspiration.
- Fire represented passion, energy, courage, and freedom.
- Water represented intuition, healing, cleansing, and love.
- Earth represented stability, abundance, and staying grounded.

Which of the four do you think is most symbolic of your nature, and why?

I think water, because nature is healing to the soul
and I love it. Nature is amazing in so many ways.
Its so peaceful, whats not to love about
it. It makes me happy.

Which element do you need most in your life right now? Explain why.

Fire and water. I need passion, energy, courage,
healing and love. I need all of those in my
life than all the rest of them. It would
be nice to have these in my life.

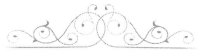

Free Association I

Fill in the blanks with the first *positive* thing that comes to mind. Go as fast as you can.

I earn _____.

I deserve _____.

I commit to _____.

I choose _____.

I look forward to _____.

I give _____.

I want _____.

I belong to _____.

Write about one of those things and what it means to you.

_____

_____

_____

_____

_____

_____

_____

_____

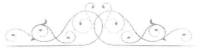

It's Okay To Ask

Many of us are reluctant to ask for help. Even when we could use an encouraging word, a favor, an introduction, a letter of recommendation, or a lesson in how to do something, we don't want to bother anyone. And some of us who want to achieve a goal don't ask anyone else who's done it how they did it! Maybe we think we're so unique or in such a different situation, the experiences of others won't apply to us. (By the way, this is almost never true.) Or maybe we're afraid to admit we don't know. (So what if we don't? The only thing to be embarrassed about is being unwilling to learn.)

Write down the names of three people and write down what you might ask them. (If you don't know the person yet, write down a description, such as "a successful entrepreneur" or "someone in the recording industry.")

Person 1: _____

What I'd like to ask for: _____.

_____

Person 2: _____

What I'd like to ask for: _____.

_____

Person 3: _____

What I'd like to ask for: _____.

_____

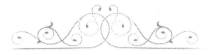

Knowing The Right People

Think about some of the kinds of people it would be good to know in order to feel happy or to reach your goals. It might be a mentor in a business or skill you're learning, an agent to represent you, a financial advisor, or someone else entirely. Write about one or more of those people here.

_____

_____

_____

_____

_____

_____

_____

Explain how it would be possible to get to know these people…or at least one of them.

_____

_____

_____

_____

_____

_____

With A Little Help From My Friends

What are some ways that you could get help with your goals from people you know right now? How could you ask them to support you…if you weren't too proud, too self-conscious, or too determined to do everything all by yourself? Write about it here.

Being There

Are there any family members or friends who might appreciate hearing from you more often? Would you like to surprise any of them with a text, a call, a card in the mail, or a surprise gift?

Is there anyone in your life who could use more support from you?

Are there people in your past—former classmates, coworkers, or neighbors—who might like to hear from you again?

Write about these people and how you might like to reach out to them here.

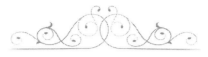

Worry Free

They say a problem doesn't go away just because you ignore it, and that's true. But some problems are going to be there whether you worry about them or not.

Stop worrying about one thing—for 24 hours, for a solid week…or for a solid month. Fill out the card below.

> ### "GET OUT OF WORRYING FREE"
> ### CARD
>
> This entitles me to not worry at all about
>
> _____my eating_____
>
> for this length of time: For as long as I'm better

If you need another one, for now or for later, here you go.

> ### "GET OUT OF WORRYING FREE"
> ### CARD
>
> This entitles me to not worry at all about
>
> _____Talk to much_____
>
> for this length of time: As long till I talked my
> heart out.

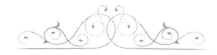

Flying High Meditation

Imagine yourself being high above your troubles and worries. You might be in a jet way above the earth (or even in a spaceship), or on the top floor of a tall building.

If you have a fear of heights, here's an alternate vision: imagine yourself being far away from them. You might be on a yacht or a private island in the middle of the ocean, for instance.

Write about that place and how you feel there, describing it as fully as you can.

_____

_____

_____

_____

_____

_____

_____

_____

_____

_____

_____

_____

_____

_____

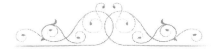

Blissing Out Meditation

Imagine yourself in the most de-stressing situation possible. You might be at a spa getting a facial or a massage, drinking a glass of wine at a café in Paris, lying in a hammock between two palm trees, or whatever your idea of being completely relaxed is. Focus on your five senses: what do you hear, see, touch, smell, and taste? Describe the experience as fully as you can.

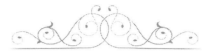

Silver Linings

$\mathbf{A}$ positive mind can see the benefits and opportunities in negative experiences. This isn't about pretending that all experiences are good. It's just about finding a little bit of good mixed in with the bad. Write about a couple of bad things that have happened…or that you're afraid might happen…and write about how they could benefit you.

Bad thing _____

The good thing about it _____.

_____

_____

_____

_____

_____

Bad thing _____

The good thing about it _____.

_____

_____

_____

_____

_____

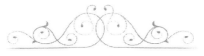

Role Call

We all play many different roles in our lives. This exercise is to help you think about a few that you're playing...that you may not even be aware of.

Choose three numbers at random between one and twenty-five.

Now flip the page and see which three words you chose.

These are three roles you are either playing now in your life, or you may play in the near future.

Below, write the words you chose in the blanks, and write about how you see yourself playing those roles, and/or imagine yourself playing those roles in the future.

_____

(role 1)

_____

_____

_____

(role 2)

_____

_____

_____

(role 3)

_____

_____

1. the king/ queen/ruler
2. the ray of sunshine
3. the romantic
4. the achiever
5. the mastermind
6. the rebel
7. the giver
8. the creator
9. the charmer
10. the scholar
11. the activist
12. the guardian
13. the boss
14. the expert
15. the free spirit
16. the coach
17. the peacemaker
18. the visionary
19. the hero
20. the force of nature
21. the healer
22. the explorer
23. the health nut
24. the celebrity
25. the dreamer

Is there a role you didn't pick through your choice of numbers…but that you choose to claim? Below, write about how you play that role in your life…or about how you will play it in the future.

Role: _____

_____

_____

_____

_____

_____

_____

_____

_____

_____

My Comfort Zone

Write about things that make you feel cozy, relaxed, or secure.

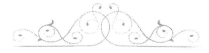

Home Sweet Home

Write about the things that you're grateful for about your home or living situation right now, even if it's not your ideal situation yet.

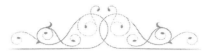

Dream Home

Imagine you're in your dream home. Write about waking up there and beginning your day. Where is it? What's the outside like? The inside? What special features does it have? Describe it in detail.

_____

_____

_____

_____

_____

_____

_____

_____

_____

_____

_____

_____

_____

_____

_____

_____

_____

_____

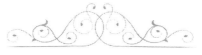

Dream Car

Imagine you have your dream car and you're taking it on a road trip. What's it like to get in and drive it? Where are you going, and what will you do there? Describe it in detail.

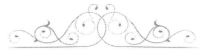

Wanderlust

Think of five places you'd like to visit. They can be close or far away. Where would you like to go? Why?

Place: _____

Reason: _____.

_____

_____

_____

_____

_____

_____

Place: _____

Reason: _____.

_____

_____

_____

_____

_____

_____

Place: _____

Reason: _____.

_____

_____

_____

_____

_____

_____

_____

Place: _____

Reason: _____.

_____

_____

_____

_____

_____

_____

_____

Place: _____

Reason: _____.

_____

_____

_____

_____

_____

_____

_____

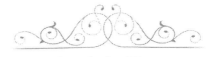

Everybody's Favorite

Imagine a situation in which you're appreciated or beloved by everyone around you. (If you already have a situation like this, that's great—just imagine another one!) This could be a situation with people you know right now or with new people. It could be at work, school, or in a social situation. Now write about it.

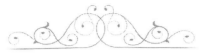

Secret Skills

This exercise is to help you become aware of all the abilities you possess. Choose three numbers between one and twenty-five.

Now flip the page and see which three skills you chose. They may be skills you know you have, skills you haven't used in a while…or ones you haven't had the opportunity to use yet. They may not be literal! Write about what those three skills might mean to you or how you might use them in the near future.

(skill 1)

(skill 2)

(skill 3)

1. negotiation
2. navigation
3. priorization
4. problem-solving
5. scheduling
6. decision-making
7. intuition
8. diplomacy
9. analysis
10. consulting
11. strategy
12. networking
13. delegation
14. note-taking
15. leadership
16. trading
17. teamwork
18. selling
19. teaching
20. storytelling
21. counseling
22. interviewing
23. innovation
24. healing
25. adaptation

Identify another skill, on this list or not, that you possess or want to possess. Why is it important? What will you do with it? Write about it below.

_____

(skill)

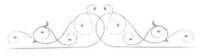

Why Not

List 10 things you'd love to try doing, just for the heck of it…and write a little bit about why you'd love to try them.

1. _____

_____

_____

2. _____

_____

_____

3. _____

_____

_____

4. _____

_____

_____

5. _____

_____

_____

6. _____

_____

_____

7. _____

_____

_____

8. _____

_____

_____

9. _____

_____

_____

10. _____

_____

_____

Daring

List 10 things you'd try if you weren't scared of failing, looking ridiculous, or wasting your time…and write a little about what you're scared of.

1. _____

_____

_____

2. _____

_____

_____

3. _____

_____

_____

4. _____

_____

_____

5. _____

_____

_____

6. _____

_____

_____

7. _____

_____

_____

8. _____

_____

_____

9. _____

_____

_____

10. _____

_____

_____

Write about a time (or a few times) you took a risk, big or small, and it paid off.

_____

_____

_____

_____

_____

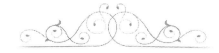

And Dare Some More

Imagine a time in the future when you take a big risk and it pays off. Write about it in the present tense...as though it's happening right now. How does it feel to take the risk? How does it feel to succeed?

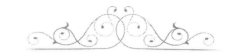

What's Theirs Is Mine

Many of us struggle with jealousy. We see others having good breaks, abundance, or experiences we don't have, and we think, "I want that!"

But what if jealousy is actually a sign that it's possible to have those things... or even better things? Knowing that it's possible is the first step to having it happen. Write about it. (You can use people's names or just say "a friend," and so on...as you like.)

I've been jealous of _____ because:

_____

_____

But in the future, I may have this, which will be even better:

_____

_____

I've been jealous of _____ because:

_____

_____

But I realize that this even better thing is a possibility in my life:

_____

_____

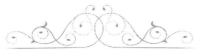

One Baby Step

Write down a huge, wildly fantastic wish or goal (Examples: win an Academy Award for screenwriting; own a luxury house on the beach.)

What's something you could achieve in the next five years to get you closer to that goal? (For example, have my script made into a big feature film, or save a certain amount of money.)

What's something you could accomplish in the next year to get closer to the achievement directly above? (For example, complete a screenplay, or get a higher-paying job.)

What's something you could do in the next three months to move you closer to the achievement directly above? (For example, outline a screenplay, or apply to one hundred jobs.)

What's a tiny baby step you could do this week to get you closer to the achievement directly above? (For example, study two award-winning scripts, or update your resumé.)

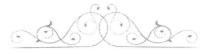

Free Association II

Fill in the blanks with the first *positive* thing that comes to mind. Go as fast as you can.

I accept _____.

I insist on _____.

I become _____.

I love _____.

I achieve _____.

I maintain _____.

I attract _____.

I create _____.

Write about one of those and what it means.

_____

_____

_____

_____

_____

_____

_____

_____

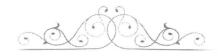

Positive Affirmations

Write some positive statements about yourself. Even if you only wish they were true, write them in the present tense, as if they're already fact. Here are some examples; you can write some more! Try to write at least five of them. If you want to write a lot of them and you run out of room, use one or more of your blank pages to write some more.

I am young, strong, healthy, and beautiful.

I am a romantic, thoughtful partner.

I am a brilliant and successful business owner.

Now write some positive affirmations about your day…or your week. Here are some examples. Keep writing in the present tense!

Today, I'm enjoying the little things.

This week, I'm getting enough time to rest and to exercise so I feel charged.

Today and every day, I'm being kind and loving to my family.

I'm having a positive and productive week.

My People

Write down the names of individuals you know (pets count), and write about why you're grateful for them.

_____

(name of person)

_____

_____

_____

_____

_____

(name of person)

_____

_____

_____

_____

_____

(name of person)

_____

_____

_____

_____

_____

(name of person)

_____

_____

_____

_____

Now write down the names of two people you don't know well…celebrities, dead famous people, or acquaintances (you can even write something like "the nice old man on the bus.") Write about why you're grateful for them.

_____

(name of person)

_____

_____

_____

_____

_____

(name of person)

_____

_____

_____

_____

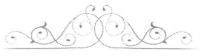

Dream Person

Write about a person you need in your life…who isn't there yet. This could be a mentor, a romantic partner, a benefactor, or anyone you choose. Write about them in as much detail as you can.

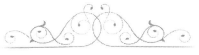

Dream Social Life

You may long for hundreds of friends...or just a few close confidantes. You may want to go to wild parties or meet somebody for coffee now and then. Write about your ideal social life here.

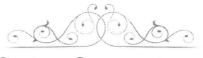

Caring Connections

Write about a time when you felt loved and supported.

_____

_____

_____

_____

_____

_____

_____

_____

Write about a time when you made someone else feel loved and supported.

_____

_____

_____

_____

_____

_____

_____

Write about a time when you were very happy all by yourself…because you are excellent company.

_____

_____

_____

_____

_____

_____

_____

_____

_____

_____

Write about some ways that you could take good care of yourself.

_____

_____

_____

_____

_____

_____

_____

_____

_____

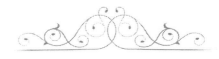

Cleansing Meditation

Many sensitive and creative people are empaths. When they spend a lot of time with sad or angry people, they absorb some of that negativity. Soon, an empath doesn't feel good at all, even though nothing's really wrong. Even a positive person by nature can experience this.

Visualize clearing yourself of negativity. You could imagine showering under a waterfall, for instance, or picture mist and clouds surrounding you evaporating.

Write about this imagined experience in detail, as though the experience was happening now. You can write about what kind of negativity you've absorbed from others if you want to, and you can write about what it feels like to have it go away.

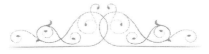

New Scripts

We can't control what happens to us, but we can control how we react to it. Many of us react to the same things in the same negative way, over and over, as if we're following some old script. It's exhausting for us, and no fun for the people around us, either.

Instead of feeling terrible, we can shrug and listen to some music. Instead of yelling, we can take a walk. Let's write some new scripts.

The next time I'm discouraged because _____.

I'm going to remind myself that _____.

and I'm going to do this: _____.

The next time I'm angry at _____ because _____

_____

_____.

I'm going to remind myself that _____.

And I'm going to do this: _____.

The next time I'm anxious because _____.

I'm going to tell myself this: _____.

and I'm going to do this: _____

_____

_____

_____.

Write some more new scripts below!

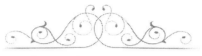

I Am Celebrated

Write about one of your favorite memories of holidays or special celebrations…or write about a few of them.

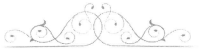

I Am Celebrating

Write about ways you'd like to celebrate some special days ahead…whether it's a holiday, a birthday, an anniversary, or a milestone, big or small.

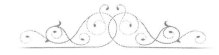

"Lighten Up" Checklist

Check all of the ways you might want to add a little more humor and laughter into your life.

- ☐ Dress up your pet and take pictures.
- ☐ Read a book of funny essays.
- ☐ Learn a kid-level joke and tell it to someone.
- ☐ Ask other people to tell you a joke.
- ☐ Learn a cheesy pickup line and use it on your partner.
- ☐ Find the humor in a frustrating situation.
- ☐ Buy a sign or a tee shirt with a saying that makes you laugh.
- ☐ Play a positive prank on someone; e.g., surprise them with something silly but good.
- ☐ Use a marker to draw goofy faces on eggs and put them back in the carton.
- ☐ Buy a package of stick-on googly eyes and get creative.
- ☐ Read a book of funny comics.
- ☐ Watch a silly comedy movie.
- ☐ Rewatch your favorite sitcom of all time.
- ☐ Watch funny videos online.
- ☐ Ask someone to tell you a funny thing that happened to them.

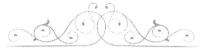

Your Lucky Time

This exercise is to help you think about the magic that lies in the days, months, and seasons of your life. Choose two numbers between one and twenty-five.

Now flip the page and see which words you chose. Write about how these particular times might turn out to be lucky for you soon.

_____

(word 1)

_____

_____

_____

_____

_____

_____

(word 2)

_____

_____

_____

_____

_____

_____

1. next January
2. this Tuesday
3. next February
4. this Wednesday
5. next March
6. this Thursday
7. next April
8. this Friday
9. next May
10. this Saturday
11. next June
12. this Sunday
13. next July
14. the next solstice (winter or summer)
15. next August
16. the next equinox (winter or summer)
17. next September
18. morning
19. next October
20. midday
21. next November
22. sunset
23. next December
24. midnight
25. this Monday

Choose another time, season, or date, on this list that you didn't already choose, but that you want to make lucky. Write about your intentions for it below.

_____

(time)

_____
_____
_____
_____
_____
_____
_____
_____

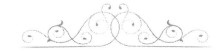

A Person For All Seasons

Write about a happy spring or summer memory of yours.

_____

_____

_____

_____

_____

_____

_____

_____

Write about a happy fall or winter memory of yours.

_____

_____

_____

_____

_____

_____

_____

_____

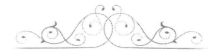

Morning Meditation

Write a prayer or meditation that you can use to start your day right. Since you might want to revise this, you might want to write lightly in pencil at first or write a rough draft on a separate piece of paper.

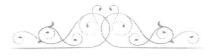

Evening Meditation

Write a prayer or meditation that you can use before you go to bed to soothe your spirit and get a good night's sleep. Again, you might want to make edits, so you might want to write the first draft in light pencil or on a separate sheet of paper.

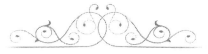

Gift Registry

Let's say you're setting up a wish list of gifts people can give you...or the universe can give you.

What are some really small things on that list? Be as specific as you like!

_____

_____

_____

_____

_____

_____

_____

What are some bigger, expensive, or fancier things on that list?

_____

_____

_____

_____

_____

_____

_____

Now what about some things that aren't actually *things*? As in, things that a person can't wrap? (Things like time, sleep, a sense of purpose, or devoted fans.)

_____

_____

_____

_____

_____

_____

Write about one or more of the things on your gift registry—tangible or intangible. What associations do you have with it? Why would you like it (or why do you need it), and how would it make you feel?

_____

_____

_____

_____

_____

_____

_____

_____

_____

_____

_____

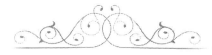

My Wishes For You

Think about some people you know and make some wishes for them. They can be the people closest to you or people you barely know.

_____

(name)

_____

_____

_____

(name)

_____

_____

_____

(name)

_____

_____

_____

(name)

_____

_____

My Wishes For The World

Write out wishes for the world and the people in it. They can be huge ("world peace") or tiny.

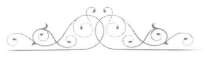

Better Than Ever

Fill in the blanks on this page!

I am better than ever at _____.

I am also better than ever at _____.

Here's something I know more about than I did a year ago: _____.

_____

Here's something I know more about than I did ten years ago: _____.

_____

Here's something I haven't done in a while, but if I started it up again, I could probably be better than ever: _____

_____

Here's another thing I would probably be amazing at if I picked it up again:

_____

_____

I'm grateful this person is in my life, and I didn't even know them ten years ago: _____.

_____

There's plenty of time for me to still _____.

_____

_____

I know my best days are ahead of me because _____.

_____

_____

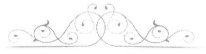

Looking Good

Fill in the blanks on this page, too!

Here are three fitness, beauty, grooming, or fashion goals I would consider making, even though I look amazing already:

1. _____
2. _____
3. _____

Here are three people whose style I really admire. (These can be people you know, or famous people, dead or alive.)

1. _____
2. _____
3. _____

Here are three things I'd love to have in my wardrobe or closet.

1. _____
2. _____
3. _____

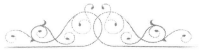

Bringer Of Joy

Write about a time when you made someone else happy—any person, in any way, big or small. (You can write about more than one if you want!)

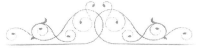

Bringer Of Truth

Write about a time when you helped someone else see the light about something or learn something new.

Word Play

Circle your favorite five words from the list below.

abundance	honor	audacity	appreciation
confidence	youth	education	self-control
joy	vitality	enthusiasm	promotion
champion	power	tradition	dignity
paradise	angel	brilliance	dedication
satisfaction	values	soul	blessing
peace	forgiveness	spontaneity	honesty
mastermind	ambition	independence	mindfulness
kindness	balance	authenticity	fulfillment
creativity	desire	clarity	positivity
faith	class	romance	discovery

On this page and the next, write about what they mean to you! Just free-write. It doesn't have to make sense!

_____

(word)

_____

_____

_____

_____

_____

(word)

_____

_____

_____

_____

_____

(word)

_____

_____

_____

_____

_____

(word)

_____

_____

_____

_____

_____

(word)

_____

_____

_____

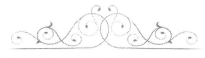

Do What You Love

Write down five ways you like to spend your free time.

1. _____

2. _____

3. _____

4. _____

5. _____

Is there any way you could do any of these things more? Write about it!

_____

_____

_____

_____

Is there any way you could actually make money doing any of these? Write about it!

_____

_____

_____

_____

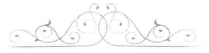

Adventures, Big And Small

List five places in your local area that you'd like to go to…or you'd like to go to more often.

1. _____

2. _____

3. _____

4. _____

5. _____

List five events (or types of events) that you might like to attend someday, though it's just a thought. Money is no object here. (For example: a professional baseball game, a state fair, the Christmas tree lighting at Rockefeller Center.)

1. _____

2. _____

3. _____

4. _____

5. _____

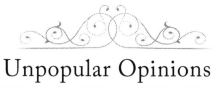

Unpopular Opinions

Write about some opinions you hold that a lot of people in your social circles wouldn't agree with, and why you hold these opinions. These can be big issues or trivial ones!

_____

(unpopular opinion 1)

_____

_____

_____

_____

_____

(unpopular opinion 2)

_____

_____

_____

_____

_____

(unpopular opinion 3)

_____

_____

_____

_____

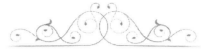

I Hold These Truths To Be Self-Evident

Write about three things you strongly believe to be true.

(Truth 1)

(Truth 2)

(Truth 3)

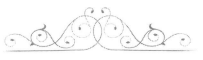

So Young

Imagine you're 105 years old. Naturally, you've slowed down a bit. You are well-cared for and think back often over your life. One day, a magical fairy visits you and grants you a very special wish.

For just one month, you get to be younger again. You get to be the age that you are now.

What would you do first? What would you enjoy doing that you probably won't be able to do at the age of 105? What is it that you love about these things? How do they make you feel? Write about it!

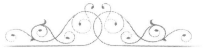

Mixed Emotions

Write about a time you cried…in a good way. (Write about more than one time if you want.)

Write about a time you laughed with someone (or write about more than one time.)

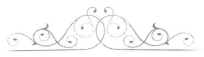

That's Rich

What ten things would you absolutely splurge on if you were very wealthy?

1. _____
2. _____
3. _____
4. _____
5. _____
6. _____
7. _____
8. _____
9. _____
10. _____

Choose one of these and explain your reasoning.

_____
_____
_____
_____
_____
_____
_____

What ten things would you never waste money on, even if you were a billionaire?

1. _____
2. _____
3. _____
4. _____
5. _____
6. _____
7. _____
8. _____
9. _____
10. _____

Choose one of these and explain your reasoning.

_____
_____
_____
_____
_____
_____
_____
_____
_____
_____
_____
_____
_____

Secret Symbols

This exercise is to help you think about what's meaningful to your identity and your life. Choose three numbers between one and twenty-five.

Now flip the page and see which three symbols you chose. Write about what they might mean to you or what they might represent in your future. You can add a drawing of the symbol if you want to.

_____

(symbol 1)

_____

_____

_____

_____

(symbol 2)

_____

_____

_____

_____

(symbol 3)

_____

_____

_____

1. sword
2. hot air balloon
3. shield
4. anchor
5. rose
6. compass
7. diamond
8. heart
9. arrow
10. bell
11. moon
12. book
13. star

14. candle
15. bolt of lightning
16. ampersand (&)
17. rainbow
18. musical notes
19. hourglass
20. feather
21. key
22. magic wand
23. crown
24. oak tree
25. four-leaf clover

Is there another symbol, on this list or not, that's meaningful to you? Claim it. Write below about what it means to you.

_____

(symbol)

_____

_____

_____

_____

A Different Story

Make a list of books you might like to read.

1. _____
2. _____
3. _____
4. _____
5. _____
6. _____
7. _____
8. _____
9. _____
10. _____

Make a list of movies or TV shows you might like to watch.

1. _____
2. _____
3. _____
4. _____
5. _____
6. _____
7. _____
8. _____
9. _____
10. _____

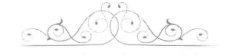

Dreams Do Come True

On this page and the next, write about some wishes or dreams that have come true in your life already.

_____

_____

_____

_____

_____

_____

_____

_____

_____

_____

_____

_____

_____

_____

_____

_____

_____

_____

Dream Day

Imagine you're living your ideal life, making a living the way you want to be making it. What is a typical day like for you? What do you do when you first get up in the morning? How do you spend the morning, and the afternoon? Who do you talk to? Where do you go? How do you spend the evening? Write all about it!

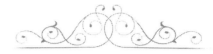

Positive Affirmations About The Universe

Write some positive statements about God, the world, or the universe. Here are three examples, but you can do these any way you want.

God has a brilliant long-term plan for me.

People are secretly conspiring to bring me more happiness.

The universe has wonderful blessings in store for me today.

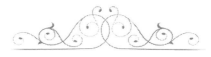

Two-Word Mantras

Try writing some two-word mantras or mottos that give you inspiration. Make the first word a verb. Here are some examples. (And yes, you are totally allowed to do some really silly ones…or all silly ones! Hey, it's your journal.)

breathe deeply

keep shining

hug dogs

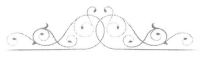

My 101 Dreams

If you're been skipping around and doing exercises out of order, it's not recommended that you do this one until you've done at least most of the other pages. The other pages will give you insights about your genuine self and what your heart truly desires.

If you think you're ready: write down 101 dreams you have for your life. You might want to do them lightly in pencil first, or on another piece of paper. There are long lines here because sometimes it helps to be specific.

These can be very small, but don't be afraid to put big ones on here, too. Go a little wild. But be warned—some of these will come true in ways you never even could've imagined.

1. _____
2. _____
3. _____
4. _____
5. _____
6. _____
7. _____
8. _____
9. _____
10. _____
11. _____
12. _____
13. _____

14. _____
15. _____
16. _____
17. _____
18. _____
19. _____
20. _____
21. _____
22. _____
23. _____
24. _____
25. _____
26. _____
27. _____
28. _____
29. _____
30. _____
31. _____
32. _____
33. _____
34. _____
35. _____
36. _____
37. _____
38. _____
39. _____
40. _____

41. _____
42. _____
43. _____
44. _____
45. _____
46. _____
47. _____
48. _____
49. _____
50. _____
51. _____
52. _____
53. _____
54. _____
55. _____
56. _____
57. _____
58. _____
59. _____
60. _____
61. _____
62. _____
63. _____
64. _____
65. _____
66. _____
67. _____

68. _____

69. _____

70. _____

71. _____

72. _____

73. _____

74. _____

75. _____

76. _____

77. _____

78. _____

79. _____

80. _____

81. _____

82. _____

83. _____

84. _____

85. _____

86. _____

87. _____

88. _____

89. _____

90. _____

91. _____

92. _____

93. _____

94. _____

95. _____

96. _____

97. _____

98. _____

99. _____

100. _____

101. _____

Looking back on your list of 101 dreams, which ones could you probably make come true in the near future?

_____

_____

_____

_____

_____

_____

What will you need in order to make these come true?

_____

_____

_____

_____

_____

_____

Of your list of 101 dreams, choose one that's really out there and almost seems unrealistic (even though it might not be!)

Now write a sentence about how it feels to have achieved it. For example: *I feel so free because I'm a millionaire*, or *I feel so excited to be interviewed about my achievements on national television.*

_____

_____

Great! Now write that sentence again, a bunch of times.

_____

_____

_____

_____

_____

_____

_____

_____

_____

_____

_____

_____

_____

_____

Now read those sentences aloud. Yep, you're going to repeat that dream aloud over and over. Read it loudly and with conviction. Notice how it makes that dream seem just a little more accessible.

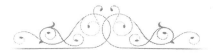

Dreams Coming True Meditation

Choose a creative way to visualize being blessed or having good things come your way. For instance, you can imagine all kinds of packages being delivered to your door, labeled with the names of your wishes...or beams of sunlight finding you and shining down on you, wherever you go, even in the night-time or on a cloudy day. Write about this visualization below, describing it in detail, including how it makes you feel.

The rest of your life
is going to be the best of your life.

Hopefully, the pages of this journal have helped you realize a few things…like how wonderful you truly are, how you have more talents and good qualities than you give yourself credit for, and how your life holds many possibilities.

Hold tight to this wisdom. Nobody can take it from you. Know in your heart that the next chapters of your life can be the best ones of all. It's an exciting time, and it starts right now.

Made in the USA
Columbia, SC
13 December 2022

73736365R00090